Topic 1

GW00418915

Global systems and global governance

Globalisation

Globalisation is a process involving the integration of national economies through a global network of trade, communications and transportation. This leads to a growth of the global economy with resulting patterns of production, distribution and consumption arising from these relationships.

Globalisation also incorporates a wider range of dimensions including social, cultural and political interactions. The process involves the spread of ideas and information across the world, but in doing so it creates a growing uniformity shared by very different places.

---

1 Distinguish between production, distribution and consumption. (AO1)   3 marks

....

....

....

2 Explain how global marketing has reduced diversity and led to more uniformity in the products and services offered to consumers globally. (AO1)   4 marks

....

....

....

....

3 Using any TWO of the factors shown in Figure 1.1, explain how each has contributed to the process of globalisation. (AO1, AO2)   8 marks

Technology

Management and labour

Communications

Political

Factors

Economic and financial

Trade agreements

Transport

Transnational corporations

....

....

....

....

....

....

....

....

....

....

....

....

....

Figure 1.1 Factors affecting globalisation

3

4 With reference to any named examples, outline the advantages and disadvantages of regional trade agreements/trading blocs for the countries involved. (AO1, AO2) 10 marks

....

....

....

....

....

....

....

....

....

....

....

Global systems

Global systems have developed from the social, economic, political and environmental **interdependence** that exists between different parts of the world. However, these systems often demonstrate the **inequalities** that exist between richer, high income economies and less developed countries.

Interdependence

5 Use an example of economic, political, social or environmental interdependence to outline its importance in the contemporary world. (AO1, AO2) 5 marks

....

....

....

....

....

....

At the conclusion of the Second World War, major international institutions including the International Monetary Fund and the World Bank were established to stabilise the world economy and to promote international economic cooperation. A General Agreement on Tariffs and Trade (GATT) to promote free trade was agreed later. GATT was succeeded in 1995 by the World Trade Organization (WTO). By the end of the twentieth century these major intergovernmental institutions became known as the Three Regulatory Pillars of the World Economic Order.

AQA

AS/A LEVEL

WORKBOOK

Geography

Human geography

Paul Abbiss and Philip Banks

FOR THE
2016
SPECIFICATIONS

HODDER
EDUCATION
LEARN MORE

Contents

WORKBOOK

(1) This workbook will help you to prepare for:

- Paper 2 of the A-level exam (Human geography)
- Paper 2 of the AS exam (Human geography and geography fieldwork investigation)
- Optional topic 'Contemporary urban environments', which appears on Paper 1 of the AS exam (Physical geography and people and the environment)

(2) Answering the questions in this workbook will help you to build your skills and meet the assessment objectives (AOs):

AO1: Demonstrate knowledge and understanding of places, environments, concepts, processes, interactions and change, at a variety of scales.

AO2: Apply knowledge and understanding in different contexts to interpret, analyse and evaluate geographical information and issues.

AO3: Use a variety of relevant quantitative, qualitative and fieldwork skills in order to:

- investigate geographical questions and issues
- interpret, analyse and evaluate data and evidence
- construct arguments and draw conclusions

(3) **For each topic** there are:

- stimulus materials, including key terms and concepts
- short-answer questions that build up to exam-style questions
- space for you to write or plan your answers
- questions which test your mathematical skills

(4) You still need to read your textbook and refer to your lesson notes and any revision guides.

(5) Marks available are indicated for all questions so that you can gauge the level of detail required in your answers.

(6) Suggested timings are given for the exam-style questions to make your practice as realistic as possible.

(7) Answers are available at: www.hoddereducation.co.uk/workbookanswers.

Note

- The subject content for AS and A-level is the same but the examination-style questions based on that subject material will be worded and/or marked differently. There is a mix of both AS and A-level questions for each topic where appropriate.
- The longer, extended-prose exam-style questions will require more space than is available in this workbook. Answer these on separate paper.
- Emboldened words or phrases appearing in this workbook are those for which a clear understanding is required. You should consider creating your own 'glossary of terms' from these words in a separate notebook.

6 Complete Table 1.1 by outlining the role of each of the three major international institutions in promoting stability, cooperation and development. (AO1, AO2)   `12 marks`

Table 1.1 Role of major intergovernmental institutions of World Economic Order

Institution	Role in promoting stability, cooperation and development within global systems
International Monetary Fund	
World Bank	
World Trade Organization	

7 Assess the success of any ONE of the institutions listed in Table 1.1 in promoting stability, growth and development. (AO1, AO2)   `8 marks`

Inequality and power relations

Unequal flows of people, capital and investment within global systems can lead to conflicts between and within countries and injustice for people and places. Understanding inequality involves recognising that global systems are shaped in unequal ways.

Inequality can be represented graphically by a Lorenz curve graph. For example, the distribution of income in a population would have cumulative percentage of population on the *x*-axis and cumulative percentage of income on the *y*-axis. A 45° line from zero to 100% represents a line of perfect equality of income among the population. In reality, income distribution in each country and globally is uneven. When plotting a Lorenz curve for income distribution of a given population, the further the curve is away from the 45° line, the more unequal is the distribution.

8 **On the blank graph below, plot a Lorenz curve showing global income distribution. Use the figures given in Table 1.2. (AO3)** **5 marks**

Table 1.2 Global income distribution (percentage of world income held by each fifth of world population)

Global population (by income group)	Poorest 20%	Next poorest 20%	Middle 20%	Second richest 20%	Richest 20%
Percentage of global income	1.5%	3.5%	6.3%	14.6%	74.1%

Figure 1.2 Lorenz curve showing inequality in global income distribution

9 **Suggest reasons why an unequal flow of (a) people, (b) money or (c) technology can lead to the inequality in global income distribution shown by the Lorenz curve you have drawn. (AO1, AO2)** **6 marks**

....

....

....

....

....

....

An alternative measure of inequality is the varying levels of **poverty** that exist globally. There is no single definition but the most common way to define absolute poverty is to base it on a minimum level of income needed to meet basic needs. This will vary from country to country but in 2008 the World Bank defined the international poverty line as $1.25 per day. (In October 2015, it reset it to $1.90 a day.)

10 Comment on the levels of poverty for the regions listed in Table 1.3 and suggest how global systems have influenced the differences and changes over time. (AO2, AO3)   6 marks

Table 1.3 Changing levels of poverty for global regions, 1981 and 2012

Region	Poverty ratio based on less than $1.25 per day PPP (= purchasing power parity) (% of population)	
	1981	2012
East Asia and Pacific	77.20	7.20
Europe and Central Asia	1.90	0.40
Latin America and the Caribbean	11.90	5.60
Middle East and North Africa	9.60	2.50
South Asia	58.80	18.70
Sub-Saharan Africa	51.50	42.60
World (average)	**44.00**	**12.70**

Source: World Bank — World Development Indicators

....

....

....

....

....

Geopolitical relationships enable some nations (and some transnational corporations) to drive global systems and gain advantages for their own interests at the expense of others.

11 Research ONE of the following intergovernmental organisations and outline the geopolitical power it has to influence global systems and affairs: *UN Security Council*; *Group of Seven (G7)*; *Group of Twenty (G20)*; *Organisation for Economic Cooperation and Development (OECD)*; *Group of 77 (G77)*. (AO1, AO2)   8 marks

....

....

....

....

....

....

....

....

....

7

International trade and access to markets

The increased access to markets has been a major contributing factor to globalisation and the global systems that exist today. The gradual erosion of barriers to trade and more recent political change in former Communist countries have opened up markets and seen the development of large transnational corporations, which operate all over the world.

Trading relationships and access to markets

12 The EU is a customs union. Explain what is meant by a customs union. (AO1)　　`2 marks`

....

....

13 Trade barriers are used by countries as a 'protectionist' measure. What are countries trying to protect? (AO1)　　`4 marks`

....

....

....

....

14 Identify TWO types of external trade barrier protecting an economy and explain how they work. (AO1, AO2)　　`6 marks`

....

....

....

....

....

....

Nature and role of transnational corporations (TNCs)

The growth of large corporations which operate in a number of countries has been a major driving force of globalisation. The spatial organisation of TNCs varies depending on the nature of their economic activity. They have become increasingly flexible in the location of their global assets.

15 How would a transnational corporation in the secondary sector (such as a vehicle manufacturer) usually organise and locate these key functions (*strategic management, production operations, research and development, sales and marketing*) of its business? (AO1, AO2)　　`4 marks`

....

....

....

....

16 What factors would influence a large manufacturing TNC in its decision to invest in a major new production plant? (AO1, AO2)   **6 marks**

....

....

....

....

17 With the use of an example, explain how TNCs are able to overcome trade barriers and gain access to different markets globally. (AO1, AO2)   **5 marks**

....

....

....

....

18 Assess the role of transnational corporations in assisting the development and growth of emerging and less developed economies. (AO1, AO2)   **10 marks**

....

....

....

....

....

....

....

....

....

....

Global governance

Global governance refers to the **rules**, **norms** and **laws** that regulate and form global systems.

Governance attempts to manage the geographical consequences for people and for natural environments in different places.

19 Outline reasons why global governance is a complex matter and difficult to achieve. (AO1)   **5 marks**

....

....

....

....

20 With reference to examples, outline the role and function of non-governmental organisations (NGOs) in global governance. (AO1, AO2)

6 marks

....
....
....
....
....
....

The United Nations (UN) is the leading agency of global governance. Since the Second World War it has aimed to promote growth and stability and to prevent and resolve conflict. More recent environmental concerns have given a greater focus on sustainable development. The UN is organised into a number of separate organisations, each with a different function.

21 Research ONE of the following bodies/agreements and outline its contribution to economic stability and/or sustainable development: *UN Development Programme (UNDP); Millennium Development Goals; UN Environmental Programme (UNEP); Sustainable Development Goals; World Summit on Sustainable Development and Agenda 21.* (AO1, AO2)

9 marks

....
....
....
....
....
....
....
....
....
....
....
....
....

Global commons

Global commons are also known as areas beyond national jurisdiction (ABNJ) and there is growing concern that they will come under increasing pressure as the global demand for resources grows. The UN recognises the essential need to have rules and regulations governing the use of the 'commons' and also to have mechanisms in place to monitor use and enforce rules.

22 List the four recognised global commons and explain why they are recognised as such by international law. (AO1) `4 marks`

....

....

....

23 Explain why the global commons are under threat from human activity and why they need to be protected. (AO1, AO2) `6 marks`

....

....

....

....

....

....

Antarctica and the Southern Ocean

The geography of Antarctica

As a continent, Antarctica is largely covered in snow and ice and is so hostile and remote that it has no permanent human residents. As a global 'common' it has no national jurisdiction but it is a centre for scientific research and unprecedented human collaboration. Antarctica has a unique landscape as well as distinctive climates and ecosystems.

24 Figure 1.3 shows an outline map of the continent of Antarctica. On this blank outline, draw in where appropriate and label the following areas. (AO1) `5 marks`

- West Antarctica
- East Antarctica
- Ronne Ice Shelf
- Ross Sea
- Weddell Sea
- Ross Sea Ice Shelf
- Antarctic Peninsula
- Transantarctic Mountains
- an approximate position of the South Pole
- Antarctic Circle (66°34'S)

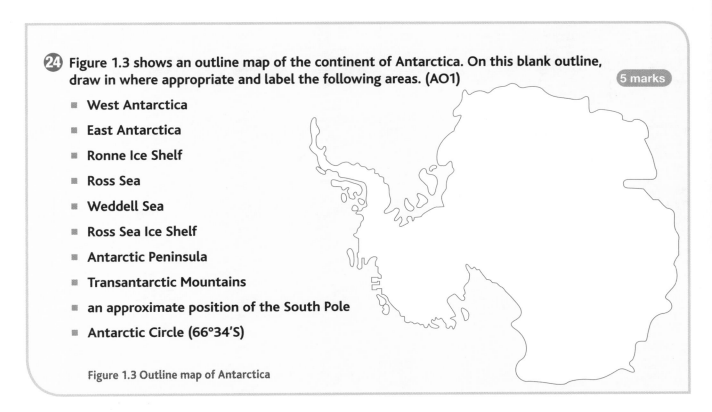

Figure 1.3 Outline map of Antarctica

25 Summarise the key physical geographical features of Antarctica by answering the following questions.

    a Describe the landscape of Antarctica. (AO1) `3 marks`

....

....

    b Explain why Antarctica is considered to be a polar desert. (AO1) `2 marks`

....

....

26 Distinguish between the Antarctic Convergence Zone and Divergence Zone. (AO1) `5 marks`

....

....

....

....

....

Threats to Antarctica

There are a number of challenges facing the environment and wilderness ecosystems of Antarctica. These threats are mostly driven by human activity.

27 Complete Table 1.4 by explaining the nature of each threat and its potential impact on the Antarctic environment. (AO1, AO2) `12 marks`

Table 1.4 Threats to Antarctica

Threat	Nature of threat and its potential impact
Climate change	
Fishing and whaling	
Search for mineral resources	
Tourism	

The governance of Antarctica

As Antarctica is a global common resource, international government organisations intervene to protect the continent from these threats, and from further exploitation. The key strategy adopted by international governance is the Antarctic Treaty System (ATS).

28 a **How did the Antarctic Treaty resolve the issue of sovereignty in Antarctica? (AO1, AO2)** `3 marks`

....

....

....

b **Outline the main features of the 1959 Antarctic Treaty. (AO1)** `6 marks`

....

....

....

....

....

....

....

29 **The Madrid Protocol was agreed in 1991 and added further protection to Antarctica. Explain why further protection was needed and assess the value added by the Protocol. (AO1, AO2)** `8 marks`

....

....

....

....

....

....

....

....

30 **Discuss the contribution of non-government organisations (NGOs) to the governance and protection of Antarctica. (AO1, AO2)** `8 marks`

....

....

....

....

....

....

....

....

Exam-style questions (A-level)

1 Explain how the International Whaling Commission has contributed to the conservation of the environment of Antarctica and the Southern Ocean. (AO1) ⏱ 5 4 marks

....

....

....

....

2 Analyse factors that have led to the increased economic, political and social interdependence seen in the contemporary world. (AO1, AO2) ⏱ 7 6 marks

....

....

....

....

....

3 Using Figure 1.4 showing trends in Antarctic temperature change and your own knowledge, assess the threats posed by global climate change on Antarctica. (AO1, AO2, AO3) ⏱ 7 6 marks

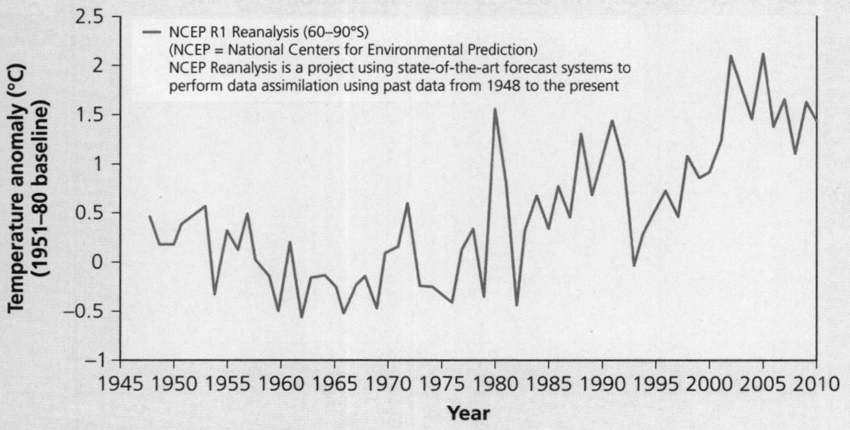

Temperature anomaly (°C) (1951–80 baseline)

— NCEP R1 Reanalysis (60–90°S)
(NCEP = National Centers for Environmental Prediction)
NCEP Reanalysis is a project using state-of-the-art forecast systems to perform data assimilation using past data from 1948 to the present

Year: 1945 1950 1955 1960 1965 1970 1975 1980 1985 1990 1995 2000 2005 2010

Figure 1.4 Antarctic temperature anomaly

....

....

....

....

....

....

....

4 'Global governance is about a world where the rule of law governs the conduct of nations.' How far do you agree with this view? (AO1, AO2) ⏱ 25 20 marks

Write your answer on a separate sheet of paper.

14

Topic 2

Changing places

The nature and importance of places

A core feature of geography entails understanding the nature of places and their characteristics. This topic is about how we engage with places, both those that are known well to us and those studied at a distance. It considers how places are known, how they are experienced and the factors and processes that develop and change their character through time.

The study of two contrasting places, as indicated under 'Place studies' on page 22, is an integral feature and should be applied throughout the whole topic.

According to geographers there are broadly three aspects of place: **location**, **locale** and the **sense of place**.

1 **What is the difference between the location, the locale and the sense of place? (AO1)**

`4 marks`

....

....

....

....

....

....

2 **Explain the relationship between place and feelings of identity, belonging and wellbeing. (AO1)**

`6 marks`

....

....

....

....

....

....

....

....

....

Different people will perceive places in very different ways. These perceptions may vary because of race, religion, ethnicity, culture, gender, age or socioeconomic background.

3 With reference to examples, compare the perspectives of 'insiders' and 'outsiders' on the nature of a place. (AO1, AO2) 8 marks

....
....
....
....
....
....
....
....

4 Explain the potential meanings of the following two different categories of place:

a Near and far places (AO1) 4 marks

....
....
....
....

b Experienced and media places (AO1) 2 marks

....
....

5 Outline how media portrayal of places may be different to the reality of life in certain places. (AO1, AO2) 6 marks

....
....
....
....
....
....

Factors contributing to the character of place

The **character of a place** refers to the combination of natural features in the landscape and the cultural characteristics of the people who occupy the place.

Endogenous and **exogenous** factors both contribute to the character of a place.

6 Explain the difference between endogenous and exogenous characteristics. (AO1) 3 marks

....
....
....

7 For a local place that you have studied, complete the boxes in Figure 2.1 by identifying factors that have contributed to the character of that place. (AO2) `10 marks`

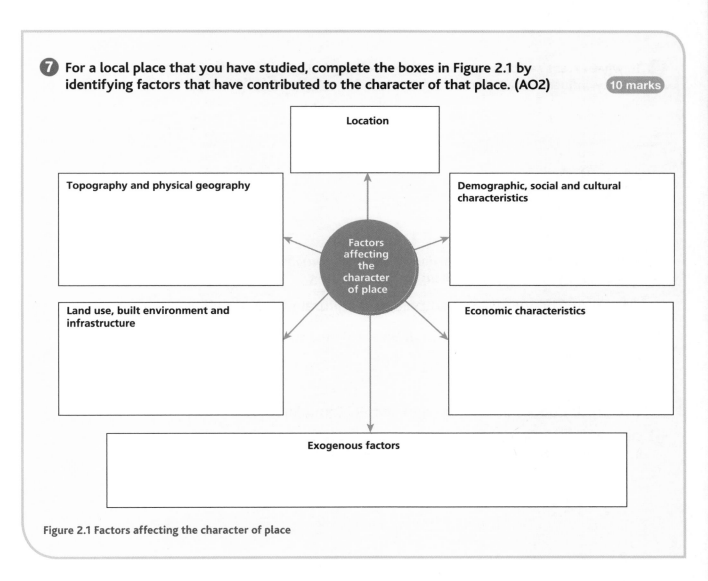

Figure 2.1 Factors affecting the character of place

Changing places

Although the location remains constant, all other aspects of a place's character change over time. To improve your understanding of the two contrasting places you have chosen to study, it is important to be aware of the factors that bring about change and also how this change affects the perceptions and lives of those living there. The factors that change places can operate at different scales.

Relationships and connections

Agents of change are those people and organisations, operating at various scales, that influence the changing character of a place.

8 Identify some of the agents of change that may influence the nature and character of places. (AO1) `5 marks`

....
....
....
....
....

9 To what extent can past and present connections, both within and beyond the locality, influence the nature and characteristics of a place? (AO1, AO2) `8 marks`

....
....
....
....
....

Answer either question 10 or question 11, depending on which aspect of 'relationship and connections' you have opted to focus on.

Option A: Changing demographic and cultural characteristics

10 Suggest reasons to explain how the demographic and cultural characteristics of a place are changed. (AO1, AO2) `6 marks`

OR

Option B: Economic change and social inequalities

11 Outline the possible impacts on the economic development and social inequality in a place resulting from external forces operating at different scales. (AO1, AO2) `6 marks`

....
....
....
....
....
....
....

Meaning and representation

Another dimension of changing places is how they are perceived by individuals or collectively (what they mean to people) and how they are represented (or seen) in society. The focus here is on people's lived experience of place(s) both in the past and at present.

12 Explain how people can develop a sense of place and what this means for their individual identities, perspectives and memories. (AO1, AO2) `6 marks`

....
....
....
....

13 Contrast the idea of a sense of place with that of perception of place. (AO1) `2 marks`

....

....

....

Perceptions of places on an international scale are more likely to be influenced by media coverage than by personal experience. Agencies external to places can operate to influence or manipulate place meanings and how they are represented at all scales.

Efforts made by external agencies to influence perception of place are often known as '**re-imaging**' or '**rebranding**'.

14 Use Figure 2.2 to help you answer the following questions.

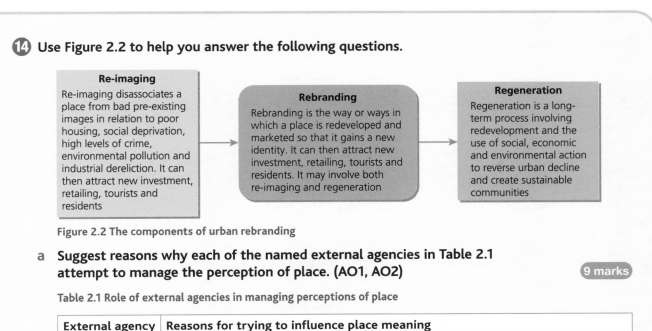

Re-imaging
Re-imaging disassociates a place from bad pre-existing images in relation to poor housing, social deprivation, high levels of crime, environmental pollution and industrial dereliction. It can then attract new investment, retailing, tourists and residents

Rebranding
Rebranding is the way or ways in which a place is redeveloped and marketed so that it gains a new identity. It can then attract new investment, retailing, tourists and residents. It may involve both re-imaging and regeneration

Regeneration
Regeneration is a long-term process involving redevelopment and the use of social, economic and environmental action to reverse urban decline and create sustainable communities

Figure 2.2 The components of urban rebranding

a Suggest reasons why each of the named external agencies in Table 2.1 attempt to manage the perception of place. (AO1, AO2) `9 marks`

Table 2.1 Role of external agencies in managing perceptions of place

External agency	Reasons for trying to influence place meaning
Local or central government (3 marks)	
Corporate bodies (3 marks)	
Local or community groups (3 marks)	

b Outline strategies that are used by external agencies to create place meanings and influence individuals' and organisations' perception of place. (AO1, AO2)
`5 marks`

....

....

....

....

Quantitative and qualitative skills

Place characteristics can be represented and supported by a whole range of quantitative and qualitative data. It is especially important to engage with and interpret a range of data when investigating your two place studies.

15 Explain the difference between quantitative and qualitative data. (AO1)
`4 marks`

....

....

....

....

One of the richest sources of quantitative data available for places in the UK is the Office for National Statistics, found online at **www.ons.gov.uk**. Census information can be particularly useful and is found at **www.neighbourhood.statistics.gov.uk**.

Table 2.2 Census data for two contrasting areas

Location	Housing (% owner occupied)	Ethnicity (% white British)	Age structure (average age)	Employment (% unemployed)
Blakenhall, Wolverhampton	62.35	23.18	38.30	7.9
Brill, Buckinghamshire	73.10	93.90	43.10	2.6

16 a Interpret and comment on the data shown in Table 2.2. (AO2, AO3)
`5 marks`

....

....

....

....

b What additional quantitative or qualitative data would you need to represent these two places to clarify your perceptions of them? (AO1, AO2)
`6 marks`

....

....

....

....

....

Images such as paintings and old or current photographs are also used to represent places. For example, photographs of places can be found on the website **www.geograph.org.uk**. The photographs include the location and the year taken.

(a)

(b)

Figure 2.3 Photographic images of contrasting places (*Topic 6, Question 16 requires you to annotate these photographs*)

17 Describe the contrasts in the two images shown in Figure 2.3 and from these representations, give your interpretation of the type of places they are. (AO2, AO3)   6 marks

....

....

....

....

....

....

Maps too — as well as determining location and locale — can be used to represent place and to influence our perception of a place, for example if it is in a built-up area or in an area surrounded by natural beauty.

18 Using Figure 6.1, the OS map of Cambridge on page 67 (in Topic 6), locate the two areas of Romsey and Histon. Use a range of quantitative and qualitative data from the sources suggested, including **www.neighbourhood.statistics.gov.uk** and **www.geograph.org.uk** to compare these two places. (*Note that on the neighbourhood statistics website, Histon is listed as Histon and Impington ward.*) (AO2, AO3)   9 marks

Write your answer on a separate sheet of paper.

Place studies

A place study involves exploring the developing character of a place. You need to undertake **two** place studies as a requirement for the exam paper. One should be a **local place** near your home or place of study, such as a neighbourhood or small rural or urban community. The other has to be a **contrasting** place, which is different economically, demographically, culturally or in terms of its political and economic organisation. It is likely to be distant but can be in the same country.

The framework of questions below suggests what you need to explore for each place and suggests sources that you might use for each question.

For questions 19–23 make notes in the tables provided and then write your answers on separate sheets of paper.

19 **Describe the location and locale of each of your place studies. (AO2)** `4 marks`

Possible sources: maps at www.ordnancesurvey.co.uk; *geospatial data (including GIS); photographs*

Local place	Contrasting place

20 **Outline a brief history of each place. (AO2)** `6 marks`

Possible sources: old maps; archive documents; text; audio-visual media; photographs

Local place	Contrasting place

21 **Contrast the demographic characteristics of each place. (AO2, AO3)** `8 marks`

Possible sources: census data (old and current) at www.neighbourhood.statistics.gov.uk; *geospatial data from the census at* http://maps.cdrc.ac.uk

Local place	Contrasting place

22 Contrast the economic characteristics of each place. (AO2, AO3)   8 marks

Possible sources: census data (old and current); newspaper text or audio-visual media; the Index of Multiple Deprivation, mapped at http://maps.cdrc.ac.uk

Local place	Contrasting place

23 Contrast the social characteristics and inequalities that exist in each place. (AO1, AO2, AO3)   8 marks

Possible sources: census data (old and current); for education, school performance information can be found at www.education.gov.uk/schools/performance/*; data on crime at* www.police.uk *and on health profiles at* www.apho.org.uk

Local place	Contrasting place

People's lived experience of the place in the past and present can be sourced orally by interviewing people or by gathering reminiscences, songs etc. Written text, audio-visual media and artistic representations can further support these experiences, as can comparing old and current photographs of the same place.

24 Examine people's lived experience of a local place that you have studied and of a contrasting place. (AO1, AO2)   10 marks

Write your answer on a separate sheet of paper.

25 Compare the changing demographic and cultural characteristics of two contrasting places that you have studied. (AO1, AO2)   10 marks

Write your answer on a separate sheet of paper.

Exam-style questions (AS, Paper 2)

1 Which of the following lists has qualitative data and quantitative data about a place in the correct columns? (AO1)

	Qualitative data	Quantitative data
A	A photograph of the place Census data about % unemployed	Average age of residents in the place Interviews recording people's opinion about the place
B	A map of the place and its locale A breakdown in proportions of ethnic minorities living there	A historical document referring to land ownership Census data recording age structure
C	Sample data recording people's assessment of environmental quality A drawing of the place from the past	Crime figures for the past 3 months A land use map of the place
D	A film documentary of the place recording life there 50 years ago Minutes from a local council meeting	A representative sample of past and current house prices Percentage of rented properties

2 For a named place that you have studied, explain ONE way in which it is represented either positively or negatively by any media source. (AO2)

....

....

....

....

3 Identify the qualitative data sources that you used to study your contrasting place and evaluate the usefulness of each in giving you a better perception of that place. (AO1, AO2)

....

....

....

....

....

....

....

....

....

....

....

....

4 With reference to a place that you have studied, assess the extent to which the character of the place has been affected by external agencies. (AO1, AO2)

Write your answer on a separate sheet of paper.

Exam-style questions (A-level, Paper 2)

5 In the context of studying places, explain how a place might be represented using qualitative data. (AO1)

 5 4 marks

6 Table 2.3 shows a range of demographic and socioeconomic data from government censuses for the central ward of Thetford, a market town in East Anglia, over a 30-year period from 1981 to 2011.

Table 2.3

Census indicator	1981	1991	2001	2011
Ethnicity (% white British)	95.80	94.30	91.59	75.00
Average age (mean)	39.01	43.60	46.02	44.10
Unemployment (%)	3.79	4.70	2.91	4.10
Home ownership (% owner occupier)	65.90	72.10	70.93	56.50
Occupation type (% managers and professionals)	19.65	21.75	20.95	16.80
Occupation type (% machine operative and unskilled)	30.26	28.40	31.68	36.70

Assess the usefulness of the data in Table 2.3 in helping you to understand the changing nature of the place. (AO2, AO3)

 8 6 marks

7 'Media representation of a place does not always reflect the reality of living there and the perceptions created can have either positive or negative effects on that place.' To what extent does this statement apply to one or more places that you have studied? (AO1, AO2)

 25 20 marks

Write your answer on a separate sheet of paper.

Topic 3

Contemporary urban environments

This topic examines the processes of urban growth and change and in particular the social and environmental challenges that accompany these processes. Environmental sustainability and social cohesion are key issues and themes that feature throughout the topic.

Urbanisation

1 **Define the term urbanisation. (AO1)** 2 marks

....

....

....

Global patterns and megacities

Table 3.1 Levels of urbanisation around the world, 2015

Region	Percentage of people living in urban areas around the world
Africa	40%
Asia	48%
Europe	73%
Latin America and Caribbean	80%
North America	82%
Oceania	70%
World average	55%

2 **Comment on the levels of urbanisation in different parts of the world as shown in Table 3.1. (AO2, AO3)** 5 marks

....

....

....

....

....

....

....

....

3 What are the main causes of urbanisation around the world? (AO1, AO2) `5 marks`

....

....

....

....

....

4 Annotate Figure 3.1 which shows the processes of suburbanisation, counter-urbanisation and urban resurgence. For each process, identify the main causes, characteristics and effects. (AO1, AO2) `9 marks`

Figure 3.1 Diagram showing urban processes: movements of people, housing and infrastructure in and around urban settlements

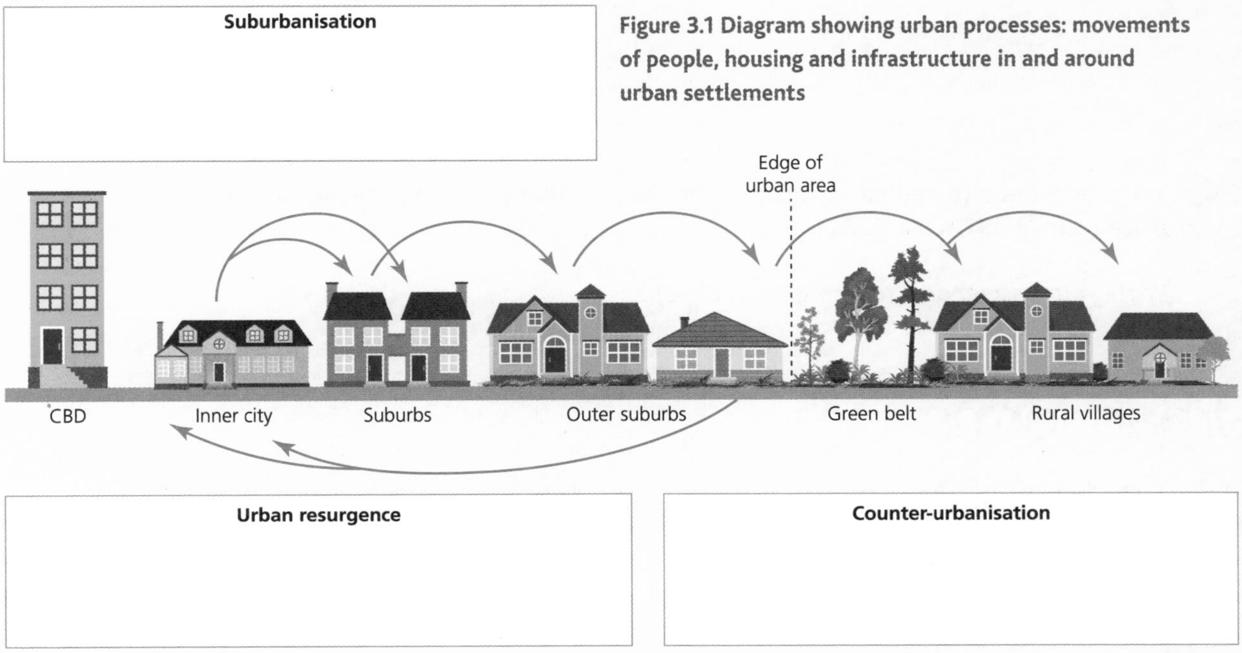

5 What is a megacity? (AO1) `1 mark`

....

6 Examine the role of megacities and world cities in global and regional economies. (AO1, AO2) `8 marks`

....

....

....

....

....

....

....

....

....

Urban change and policy

7 Explain what is meant by decentralisation. (AO1) `2 marks`

....

....

8 Analyse the relationship between deindustrialisation and the rise of the service economy and assess the impact of these two processes on urban areas. (AO1, AO2)

....

....

....

....

....

....

....

....

....

....

9 With reference to explicit strategies, evaluate urban policy and regeneration in Britain since 1979. (AO1, AO2)

Write your answer on a separate sheet of paper.

Urban forms

Urban form refers to the physical features that characterise built-up areas. These include the shape, size, density and configuration of land use in urban settlements.

Contemporary characteristics

10 In the space below draw two models of urban morphology, one representing more developed cities and one more typical of less developed cities. (AO1, AO2)

11 Compare the characteristics of cities in high income countries with those in developing parts of the world. (AO1, AO2) 6 marks

....

....

....

....

....

12 With reference to examples, analyse the physical and human factors that have shaped the spatial patterns of land use, segregation and diversity in contrasting urban areas. (AO1, AO2) 9 marks

Write your answer on a separate sheet of paper.

New urban landscapes

Urban morphology and land use have changed significantly in recent years as a result of economic and social forces and political intervention. This is typified in the UK where many city centres have experienced decline because of the decentralisation of residential and business areas and the growth of out-of-town retail, business and industrial parks. Strategies have been introduced by central and local government to reverse this decline.

13 For any ONE of the defined new types of urban landscape listed below, describe the characteristics and account for their development in recent years. (AO1, AO2) 6 marks

a   Town centre mixed developments

b   Edge cities

c   Fortress landscapes

....

....

....

....

....

....

14 Identify some of the key features expected to be seen in a post-modern Western city. (AO1) 5 marks

....

....

....

....

....

Social and economic issues associated with urbanisation

The key social and economic issues associated with urbanisation are poverty and **economic inequality** leading to deprivation, **social segregation** and **cultural diversity**.

15 Explain why economic inequality exists as a key issue in many different urban areas. (AO1, AO2)

5 marks

....

....

....

....

....

16 Analyse either social segregation *or* cultural diversity as an issue in contrasting urban areas. (AO1, AO2)

10 marks

....

....

....

....

....

....

....

....

....

Urban climate

Urban areas create weather patterns and a distinct localised climate known as a microclimate. Air quality is often poor in many towns and cities. Particulate matter and photochemical smog are particular problems associated with urban environments.

17 Define what is meant by microclimate. (AO1)

2 marks

....

....

18 Describe the impact that the urban area has on temperatures compared to surrounding rural areas. (AO1, AO2)

4 marks

....

....

....

19 In Table 3.2, outline the reasons for increased frequency and intensity of precipitation, thunderstorms and fogs in urban environments. (AO1, AO2) `9 marks`

Table 3.2 Increased frequency and intensity of weather phenomena in urban areas

Weather type	Reasons for increased frequency and intensity in urban areas
Precipitation (3 marks)	
Thunderstorms (3 marks)	
Fog (3 marks)	

20 Examine the effects of urban structures on wind speed, direction and frequency. (AO1, AO2) `6 marks`

Urban drainage

21 **a** **Contrast the surface and catchment characteristics of an urban drainage area with those of a rural area. (AO1)**

....

....

....

   b **Explain the effects of the catchment characteristics and water usage in urban areas on the urban water cycle. (AO1, AO2)**

....

....

....

....

22 **Explain the meaning of 'sustainable urban drainage systems' (SUDS) and suggest methods using SUDS to manage urban catchment areas. (AO1, AO2)**

....

....

....

....

....

Urban waste and its disposal

Waste generation and its disposal cause enormous problems for local authorities and urban planners. The problems are predicted to intensify as waste levels increase by around 7% as a global average.

Another important consideration is the relationship between levels of waste and economic development and the importance of individual lifestyles and attitudes. Rapid population growth in low income countries will inevitably increase waste generation. However, the waste produced per person in high income countries is much higher. The amount of waste produced by society is more a function of its wealth and level of consumerism than of its population size.

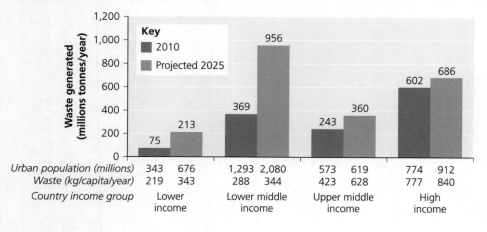

Waste generated (millions tonnes/year)	2010	Projected 2025
Lower income	75	213
Lower middle income	369	956
Upper middle income	243	360
High income	602	686

	Lower income	Lower middle income	Upper middle income	High income
Urban population (millions)	343 / 676	1,293 / 2,080	573 / 619	774 / 912
Waste (kg/capita/year)	219 / 343	288 / 344	423 / 628	777 / 840

Figure 3.2 Trends in income waste generation

㉓ **Analyse the trends in waste generation shown in Figure 3.2. (AO2, AO3)**   6 marks

There are alternative approaches to waste management. Figure 3.3 shows the waste management hierarchy of different approaches. These are ranked from the most preferred option in terms of reducing environmental impact to the least preferred.

㉔ **Annotate Figure 3.3 by outlining what each approach involves and why some waste management methods are preferred and encouraged while others are discouraged. (AO1, AO2)**   10 marks

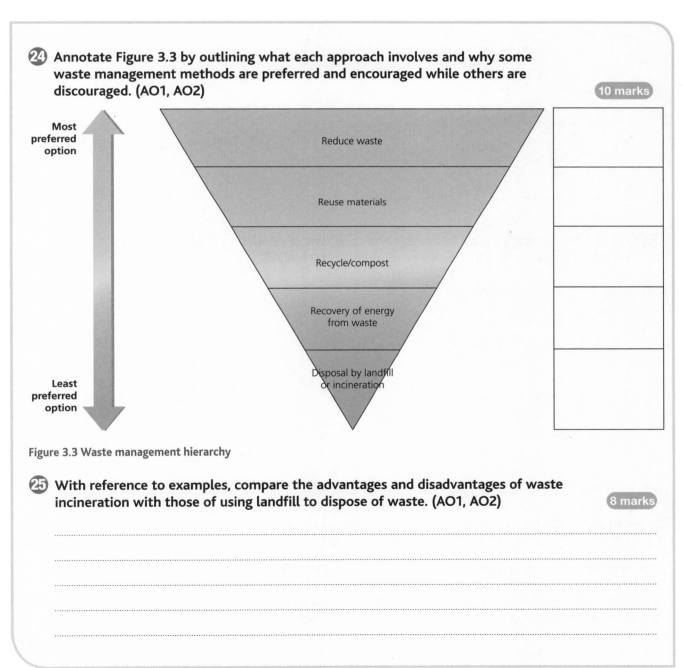

Figure 3.3 Waste management hierarchy

㉕ **With reference to examples, compare the advantages and disadvantages of waste incineration with those of using landfill to dispose of waste. (AO1, AO2)**   8 marks

Other contemporary urban environmental issues

26 **Explain why dereliction is an issue in some urban areas. (AO1)**　　`5 marks`

....

....

....

....

....

....

27 **Examine the causes and consequences of water pollution. (AO1, AO2)**　　`7 marks`

....

....

....

....

....

....

....

....

28 **Discuss the strategies used to manage the problems of *either* air pollution or water pollution *or* dereliction in urban environments. (AO1, AO2)**　　`8 marks`

....

....

....

....

....

....

....

Sustainable urban development

A **sustainable urban environment** is one providing employment, a high quality of life, a clean, healthy environment and fair governance for all its citizens both now and in the long term. It will have a low ecological footprint and reduced impact on both the surrounding and the global environment.

To consider the sustainability and environmental impacts of major urban areas it is useful to think of the town or city as a system (as shown in Figure 3.4) with inputs from both local and global sources and with outputs which are released from the city into the local and global environment.

29 a Annotate the diagram shown in Figure 3.4(a) to suggest inputs that might be taken into the urban area from local or global sources and outputs that are released into the surrounding or global environment. (AO1, AO2) **6 marks**

   b Annotate the diagram shown in Figure 3.4(b) to suggest how the inputs might be adjusted and to outline the loops out and back into the more sustainable city. (AO1, AO2) **4 marks**

(a) Unsustainable city/urban environment

(b) More sustainable city/urban environment

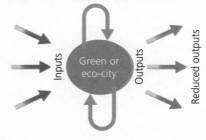

Figure 3.4 The urban area as a system

30 Explain what is meant by the concept of liveability. (AO1) **4 marks**

....

....

....

31 With reference to examples, assess the strategies that are used to develop more sustainable cities. (AO1, AO2) **10 marks**

....

....

....

....

....

....

....

....

....

....

....

Exam-style questions (AS, Paper 1)

1 What is photo-chemical pollution? Circle the correct answer. (AO1)

   A Pollution found in cities as a result of sunlight reacting with nitrogen oxides and other hydrocarbons from vehicle exhaust fumes resulting in the production of ozone

   B A name for the pollution found above an urban area resulting from the mix of different chemical gases emitted into the atmosphere from the city

   C A type of air pollution resulting from tiny particles of solid or liquid matter suspended in the atmosphere

   D A type of water pollution resulting from chemical effluents leaking into drainage systems from industrial premises

2 Outline reasons for urban resurgence. (AO1)

(a) 2000

(b) 2025

Figures 3.5 Distribution of megacities, 2000–2025 (predicted)

3 Comment on the predicted changes in the distribution of megacities between 2000 and 2025 as shown in Figure 3.5. (AO2, AO3) ⏱ 6 6 marks

....

....

....

....

....

....

4 Analyse the impacts of deindustrialisation on urban areas. (AO1, AO2) ⏱ 11 9 marks

....

....

....

....

....

....

....

....

....

....

....

....

....

5 'River restoration and conservation in damaged urban catchments will enhance environmental quality as well as improve urban drainage.' With reference to a specific project, discuss this statement and evaluate the project outcomes. (AO1, AO2) ⏱ 20 20 marks

Write your answer on a separate sheet of paper.

Exam-style questions (A-level, Paper 2)

6 What are the key features of counter-urbanisation? Circle the correct answer. (AO1)   20 1 mark

A During the 1950s and 1960s large-scale construction of council housing took place on the suburban fringe.

B One of the negative effects of counter-urbanisation is that it creates urban sprawl as it infringes on areas of the green belt.

C Counter-urbanisation leads to the social, economic and structural regeneration of the urban area following a period of decline.

D Counter-urbanisation affects the layout of rural settlements as modern, mainly private housing estates are built on the edge of small settlements.

7 Analyse the trends in urbanisation between 1950 and 2050 (predicted) shown in Figure 3.6. (AO2, AO3)

⏱ **7** **6 marks**

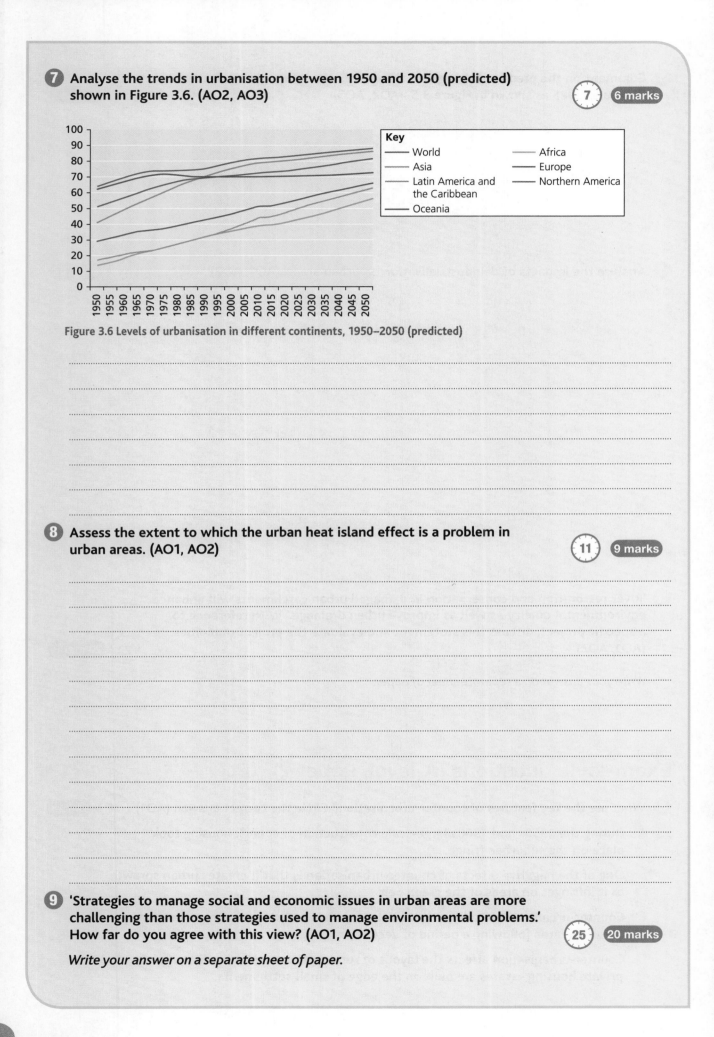

Figure 3.6 Levels of urbanisation in different continents, 1950–2050 (predicted)

....

....

....

....

....

....

....

8 Assess the extent to which the urban heat island effect is a problem in urban areas. (AO1, AO2)

⏱ **11** **9 marks**

....

....

....

....

....

....

....

....

....

....

....

....

9 'Strategies to manage social and economic issues in urban areas are more challenging than those strategies used to manage environmental problems.' How far do you agree with this view? (AO1, AO2)

⏱ **25** **20 marks**

Write your answer on a separate sheet of paper.

Topic 4

Population and the environment

Environment and population

Environmental conditions influence patterns of food production globally and consequently determine population distribution and density patterns. To support a given sedentary or nomadic population sustainably, the environmental conditions need to be favourable enough to provide sufficient food and water for that population. Agricultural systems and farming methods have been adapted to try to maximise productivity given key environmental variables, in particular the limiting factors presented by climate and soils.

1 **Distinguish between the terms population distribution and population density. (AO1)** `3 marks`

....

....

....

2 **Figure 4.1 shows opposites in farming systems. Complete the blank spaces with either the given name or the explanation of this farming method. (AO1)** `12 marks`

Food production

How the systems are classified	Agricultural food production systems	
By purpose of production	Produce enough to survive/no surplus/use food to trade for other necessities	Surpluses yield profit from sales of produce; relies heavily on investment and entrepreneurship
By the manner of production	Intensive	Extensive
By the nature of the inputs	Dominant inputs are workers and their use of hand-held tools	Dominant inputs are agricultural chemicals (fertilisers, pesticides, herbicides) and processing machinery to gain high yields per hectare
By the type of products	Arable	Pastoral

Figure 4.1 Agricultural production systems

3 Figure 4.2 shows how productivity might be affected by the level of inputs into a farming area and the size of the area itself. Annotate each diagram by completing the blank inputs, giving a brief explanation of each system and providing an example of each (from anywhere in the world). (AO1, AO2)　　9 marks

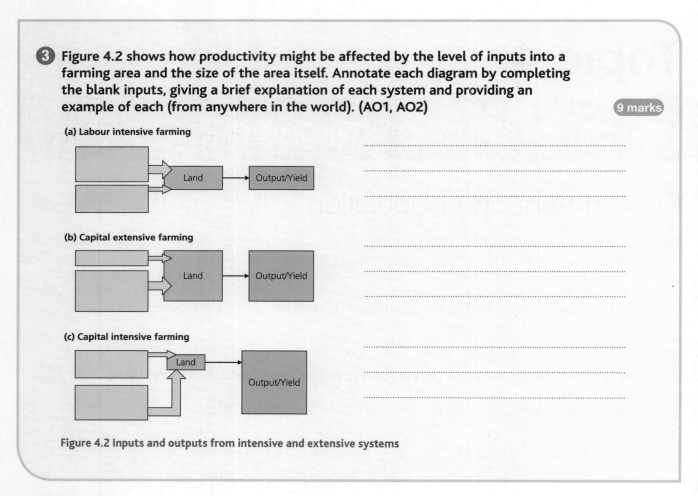

(a) Labour intensive farming

....
....
....

(b) Capital extensive farming

....
....
....
....

(c) Capital intensive farming

....
....
....

Figure 4.2 Inputs and outputs from intensive and extensive systems

Climate

Climate is defined as a region's long-term weather pattern. The most important features of weather that affect food production are precipitation patterns (both quantity and seasonal distribution) and temperature. The following aspects are also important in determining the type of crops grown and livestock reared: sunshine hours, humidity, prevailing wind direction and speeds.

4 For *any* TWO of the following aspects of climate explain how they affect food production and the species that are selected for cultivation.　　8 marks

　a　Water supply (AO1, AO2)

　b　Temperature (AO1, AO2)

　c　Wind velocity (AO1, AO2)

　d　Levels of sunlight (AO1, AO2)

....
....
....
....
....
....
....
....

Soils

There is a lot of specialised terminology in this topic.
Knowing the precise meaning of the terms will help
with your learning.

⑤ Complete Table 4.1 as a glossary of key terms. (AO1)

Table 4.1 Key terms associated with soils

Term	Definition
	a major soil group with well-defined features associated with a particular climatic regime and covering a wide geographical region
waterlogging	
	the accumulation of soluble salts (e.g. of sodium and magnesium) in the soil — often to toxic levels preventing plant growth
soil structure	

**⑥ Figure 4.3 shows a basic diagram of soil depth known as a soil profile. Each layer
in the profile is known as a soil horizon. Label and annotate each horizon and
explain for each why the soil might be different in this part of its profile. (AO1, AO2)** 10 marks

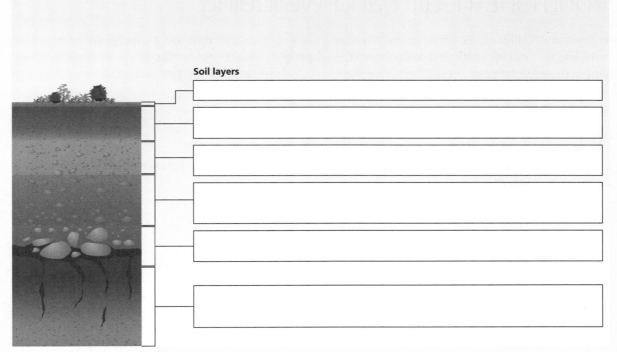

Figure 4.3 A soil profile

**⑦ Outline both the advantages and the limiting factors for agricultural productivity
given by a specific zonal soil type that you have studied. (AO1, AO2)** 6 marks

....
....
....
....
....

Food security

8 Using examples that you have studied, discuss strategies that could be adopted to ensure food security. (AO1, AO2)

8 marks

Environment, health and wellbeing

There are direct and indirect links between the physical environment and the overall health and wellbeing of the people living in that environment. For example, shortages of water and, in turn, food supply will adversely affect people's health but methods to increase productivity may have adverse impacts on health as well.

Health

9 Explain the link between social and economic development and epidemiological transition. (AO1, AO2)

6 marks

----

10 Examine the relationship between incidence of disease or poor health and any ONE aspect of the environment, including air quality and water quality. (AO1, AO2)

10 marks

Write your answer on a separate sheet of paper.

Global prevalence and distribution of diseases

11 As an introductory activity for this section, sort the following list of diseases into one of the two columns in Table 4.2: *obesity; Type 2 diabetes; malaria; tuberculosis (TB); lung cancer; meningitis, Ebola; coronary heart disease; HIV/AIDs; Alzheimer's disease.* (AO1) **5 marks**

Table 4.2 List of biologically transmitted and non-communicable diseases

Biologically transmitted diseases	Non-communicable diseases

12 Select any ONE of the diseases listed in Table 4.2 and answer the following questions.

a Account for its global prevalence and distribution. (AO1) **6 marks**

b Discuss the impacts on health and wellbeing of having this disease. (AO1, AO2) **8 marks**

c Examine the strategies used to prevent the spread of this disease. (AO1, AO2) **8 marks**

Write your answers on a separate sheet of paper.

Population change

Human population is dynamic; there are constant changes at all scales of study. For example, world population has constantly and exponentially grown over the past two centuries; however, some individual countries have declining populations and the rates of growth vary enormously between different nations. Population can change in the following ways:

- Size (increase or decrease)
- Spatial distribution — where the population is located and population density
- Structure — the age and gender distribution of a population, represented by population pyramids which can alter their shape over time

There are two main components contributing to population change: **natural change** and **migration change**.

13 Distinguish between natural population change and migration and explain how these two components are linked in influencing population change. (AO1) **4 marks**

43

Natural change

14 Complete Table 4.3 by inserting correct terms or definitions for key demographic indicators. (AO1)

Table 4.3 Key demographic indicators

Term	Definition
birth rate	
	the number of deaths per 1,000 of the population per year
fertility rate	
	the number of deaths of children under the age of .... year(s) per 1,000 .... per year
life expectancy	

15 Complete the diagram of the demographic transition model (DTM) outlined in Figure 4.4 by identifying stages of development and annotating all parts as fully as possible. (AO1)

5 marks

16 In the box underneath the demographic transition model, sketch outline diagrams of population pyramids as they would appear at each stage of the model. (Draw in age lines at 15 and at 65). (AO1, AO2)

5 marks

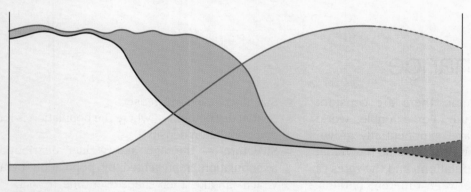

Figure 4.4 Outline of the demographic transition model

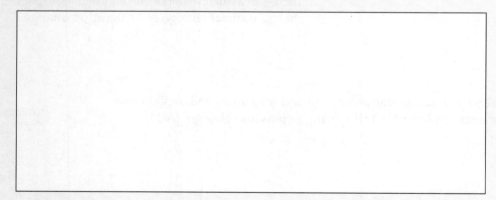

17 Study the data in Table 4.4, which shows selected population indicators for five countries at different stages of development.

Table 4.4 Population indicators for countries at different stages of development, 2015

Country	Birth rate	Death rate	Natural change	Infant mortality rate	DTM stage
Uganda	43	10	3.3	38	
India	20	7	1.3	38	
Argentina	18	8	1.0	11	
USA	13	8	0.4	6	
Germany	9	11	−0.2	3	

a Complete Table 4.4 by estimating which stage of the demographic transition model each country lies in, based on the population indicators. (AO2) 3 marks

b Comment on the varying rates of natural change shown in Table 4.4. (AO2, AO3) 5 marks

18 What causes a 'demographic dividend' and what impacts might it have on a country's economy? (AO1, AO2) 10 marks

International migration

International migration is defined as the movement of people across a specified boundary to establish a new permanent or semi-permanent residence. Although migration is seen as a separate component of population change, it will have an indirect effect on natural change and will also influence population structure.

The causes of migration are usually categorised as push and pull factors, with push factors located at the country of origin and pull factors at the destination country.

19 Distinguish between the terms asylum seeker, economic migrant and refugee, which are used to determine certain types of migrant. (AO1) `6 marks`

....

....

....

....

....

....

....

....

....

20 In Table 4.5, outline two causes of migration in each of the four categories identified by the boxes. (AO1) `8 marks`

Table 4.5 Causes of migration

Causes	Push factors	Pull factors
Environmental	1. 2.	1. 2.
Socioeconomic	1. 2.	1. 2.

21 How does migration influence natural population change? (AO1) `4 marks`

....

....

....

....

....

There can be many consequences resulting from international migration. The specification looks at the demographic, environmental, social, economic, health and political implications of migration.

22 Using a case study of a migration event that you have researched, discuss the implications for the countries of origin and destination involved. (AO1, AO2) `12 marks`

Write your answer on a separate sheet of paper.

Population ecology

As a species humans are, in many ways, subject to the same factors that affect population growth in other species. Humans are only different in that we are more conscious of our own population growth and of the consequences of our interaction with the environment in terms of resource use. We are also the only species that can influence environmental change on a global scale.

23 Complete Table 4.6 to demonstrate your understanding of key specialist terms associated with population ecology. (AO1) `3 marks`

Table 4.6 Key terms associated with population ecology

Term	Definition
carrying capacity	
	a measure of the demand placed by humans on all the Earth's resources and natural ecosystems

Population growth, size and structure and relationship with resources

24 What is meant by exponential growth and why has the world's human population experienced this type of growth over the past 200 years? (AO1) `4 marks`

....

....

....

....

25 Explain the concepts of optimum population, overpopulation and underpopulation and how each can affect the standard of living of a population. (AO1, AO2) `6 marks`

....

....

....

....

....

....

....

It is not only population size that impacts on available resources. Different population structures will have different implications for the use of resources (including services).

Table 4.7 lists the same countries used in Table 4.4 to analyse population data. This table presents data showing the relationship between the **ecological** **footprint** and **productive bio-capacity** of each nation. Both sets of figures are measured by **global hectares** per capita (gha/capita) — the common accounting unit for ecological footprint and bio-capacity. (A global hectare encompasses the average productivity of all biologically productive land and sea areas, e.g. cropland, forests, fisheries, in the world in a given year.)

Table 4.7 Ecological footprint and productive bio-capacity, 2015

Country	Ecological footprint of consumption (gha/capita)	Bio-capacity (gha/capita)	Ecological deficit/reserve (gha/capita)
Uganda	1.2	0.9	−0.30
India	1.2	0.5	−0.70
Argentina	3.1	7.5	4.40
USA	8.2	3.9	−4.30
Germany	5.3	1.9	−3.40
World average	2.7	1.8	−0.9

26 **Comment on the data in Table 4.7 and the implications they hold for the relationship between the population of these countries and their use of resources available to them. (AO1, AO2, AO3)**

8 marks

....

....

....

....

....

....

....

....

....

Population and resources balance

Figure 4.5 shows the population, resources and pollution model.

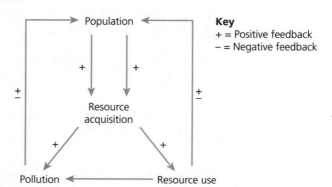

Figure 4.5 The population, resources and pollution model

27 Explain why there is both positive and negative feedback between pollution and population and resource use and population. (AO1, AO2) 6 marks

....

....

....

....

....

....

Figure 4.6 shows two blank diagrams which represent the contrasting perspectives of Thomas Malthus and Ester Boserup on population growth over time and its relationship with food supply.

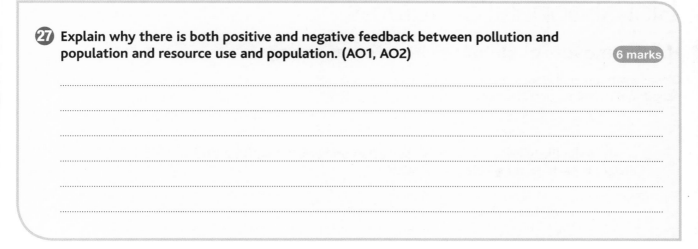

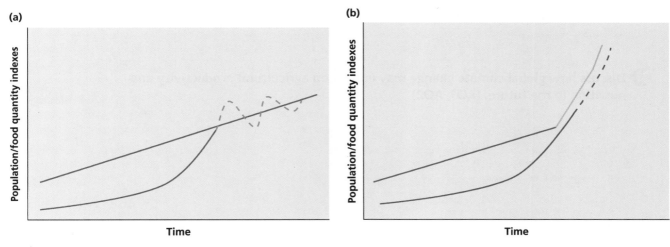

(a)

(b)

Figure 4.6 Malthus and Boserup diagrams showing the relationship between population growth and food supply

28 a Identify which diagram represents the Malthusian perspective on the population–resource relationship and which represents the views of Ester Boserup. (AO1) 1 mark

....

b Annotate each diagram clearly to outline the perspective of each theorist. (AO1, AO2) 5 marks

29 Assess the extent to which the perspectives of both Malthus and Boserup are reflected in the context of the population–resource relationship of the twenty-first century. (AO1, AO2) 8 marks

....

....

....

....

....

....

....

....

Global population futures

Health impacts of global environmental change

Global environmental change may threaten the health of
people in different parts of the world.

30 Analyse the likely impacts of ozone depletion on human health for populations in
different parts of the world. (AO1, AO2)

6 marks

....

....

....

....

....

....

....

31 Discuss how global climate change may impact on agricultural productivity and
nutrition in the future. (AO1, AO2)

8 marks

....

....

....

....

....

....

....

....

....

....

....

Prospects and projections

32 Outline the factors that will influence the rate of global population growth during
the twenty-first century. (AO1, AO2)

6 marks

....

....

....

....

....

....

....

33 Comment on the changes in the distribution of global population as projected by the UN, shown in Table 4.8. (AO2, AO3)

8 marks

Table 4.8 Projected changes in the world's population distribution by region, 2015–2100

Region	Population (millions)			
	2015	**2030**	**2050**	**2100**
Africa	1,186	1,679	2,478	4,387
Asia	4,393	4,923	5,267	4,889
Europe	738	734	707	646
Latin America and the Caribbean	634	721	784	721
North America	358	396	433	500
Oceania	39	47	57	71
WORLD	7,349	8,501	9,725	11,213

Source: UN Population Division (2015)

Exam-style questions (A-level)

1 What happens to the shape of the population pyramid for a country as it progresses from stage 2 to stage 3 of the demographic transition model? Circle the correct answer. (AO1)

A The base remains wide and the apex narrow but the sides become straighter as death rate falls so it looks more like a triangle.

B The apex gets taller and broader as more people live longer and the base remains broad and unchanged as birth rates are still high.

C The base becomes slightly narrower and the middle section of economically active people becomes wider so the pyramid is oval shaped.

D There are many more elderly people and fewer young people so the pyramid becomes top heavy with more elderly dependants than young dependants.

2 Table 4.9 shows the differences between the top six causes of death in low income countries compared to high income countries.

Comment on the differences between the top six causes of death as shown in Table 4.9. (AO2, AO3)

7 **6 marks**

Table 4.9 Main causes of death in low income and high income countries

In rank order (deaths per 100,000 population)			
Low income countries		**High income countries**	
Cause	**Deaths/100,000**	**Cause**	**Deaths/100,000**
Lower respiratory infections (e.g. pneumonia)	91	Ischaemic heart disease	158
HIV/AIDs	65	Stroke	95
Diarrhoeal diseases	53	Cancer (trachea/lung)	49
Strokes	52	Alzheimer's disease	42
Ischaemic heart disease	39	Chronic obstructive pulmonary disease (COPD)	31
Malaria	35	Lower respiratory infections	31

Source: World Health Organization

....
....
....
....
....
....

3 Assess the importance of managing soil problems for future agricultural productivity. (AO1, AO2)

11 **9 marks**

....
....
....
....
....
....
....
....
....

4 'Controlling population growth should be the most important objective for world leaders in order to ensure there is a sustainable balance between the size of the human population and resource use.' How far do you agree with this statement? (AO1, AO2)

25 **20 marks**

Write your answer on a separate sheet of paper.

Topic 5

Resource security

Resource development

The uneven distribution of the Earth's natural resources is a key geographical feature and one of the defining issues of the human–physical geography interface. Population growth combined with increasing affluence in many parts of the world has meant increasing demand for water supplies, energy and minerals. Their importance for human survival and development has led to more transfers of water on a local and regional level, and on a global scale for energy and mineral resources, to ensure resource security.

1 **What is a resource? (AO1)** 2 marks

....

....

2 **What is meant by resource security? (AO1)** 3 marks

....

....

....

3 **With the use of examples, outline the difference between flow resources and stock resources. (AO1)** 4 marks

....

....

....

....

....

The diagram in Figure 5.1 is known as a McKelvey box. It shows that only a certain proportion of all the stock resources on the planet are available to us as 'reserves' at any one time.

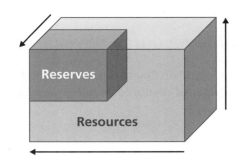

Reserves

Resources

Figure 5.1 McKelvey box showing the distinction between resources and reserves

4 **Annotate the three arrows on Figure 5.1 with three sets of criteria that determine when a resource becomes an available reserve. (AO1)** 3 marks

53

5 Explain the difference between a measured reserve and an inferred resource. (AO1) `4 marks`

....

....

....

....

....

Hydraulic fracturing development in the UK

In August 2015 and May 2016, the British government awarded licences to energy companies such as Cuadrilla and Third Energy to explore for shale oil and gas across large parts of England, to be extracted using the controversial process of **hydraulic fracturing** (otherwise known as '**fracking**'). This exploration is likely to affect large areas in Lancashire, North Yorkshire and the East Midlands but also some in the South, including areas in Dorset, Somerset, Wiltshire, Sussex, Surrey and the Isle of Wight.

6 Using the information in the extract above:

a How might this affect 'peak oil and gas' production within the UK? (AO1, AO2) `5 marks`

....

....

....

....

....

b Suggest why some areas will become 'resource frontiers' and what this will mean for them. (AO1, AO2) `6 marks`

....

....

....

....

....

....

Sustainable resource development

7 To what extent do Environmental Impact Assessments contribute to the sustainability of resource development? (AO1) `6 marks`

....

....

....

....

....

Natural resource issues

Patterns of production, consumption and trade

Energy production and consumption are usually measured in millions of tonnes of oil equivalent (Mtoes). In other words, this is all the energy of all types used in a country, measured by the weight of oil needed to produce that amount of energy. Table 5.1 gives a list of the top six total producers by country, the top six total consumers, and the top six exporting and importing countries.

Table 5.1 Top energy producers, consumers and traders, 2015 (measured in Mtoes)

Top energy producers	Mtoes	Top energy consumers	Mtoes	Top energy net exporters	Mtoes	Top energy net importers	Mtoes
China	2,640	China	3,101	Russia	613	China	483
USA	2,012	USA	2,196	Saudi Arabia	431	Japan	418
Russia	1,341	India	882	Australia	239	India	300
Saudi Arabia	650	Russia	718	Canada	204	USA	255
India	593	Japan	435	Indonesia	176	South Korea	238
Canada	456	Germany	305	Norway	170	Germany	200

8 Comment on the data in Table 5.1 and what this means for movements of energy supplies around the world. (AO2, AO3)　　8 marks

....

....

....

....

....

....

....

....

....

....

9 Outline both the physical factors and the human factors that determine global water availability. (AO1)　　4 marks

....

....

....

....

10 Suggest reasons why the demand for water is much higher in some parts of the world compared to others. (AO1, AO2)　　6 marks

....

....

....

....

....

....

Geopolitics

11 What is meant by geopolitics? (AO1) `2 marks`

....

....

12 Select ONE natural resource (from *water*, *mineral ores* or a *named fossil fuel*) and examine how geopolitics influences the trade and management of the resource you have chosen. (AO1, AO2) `8 marks`

....

....

....

....

....

....

....

....

....

Water security

Sources

13 Identify the main sources of water available for humans to use. (AO1) `2 marks`

....

....

14 Explain the meaning of water stress and the characteristics associated with it. (AO1) `5 marks`

....

....

....

....

....

Sustainability issues and water management

Sustainability of water supplies can be achieved by using strategies to increase water supply where it is needed and by using strategies to reduce demand where it is overused or wasted.

In areas of **water stress** and **water scarcity**, strategies need to be deployed to increase the supply of water to meet the demand.

15 Examine the various strategies that are used to increase water supply. (AO1, AO2)   8 marks

One strategy used to increase water supply in a catchment area is to store water in a reservoir, created by damming a river valley. This may give other potential advantages such as flood control and the capacity to generate electricity by hydroelectric power (HEP).

16 Outline the main environmental impacts caused by damming a river to create a reservoir. (AO1, AO2)   5 marks

17 Explain the meaning of each of the following and how they contribute to sustainable water management.

   a   Virtual water trade (AO1)   4 marks

b   Greywater (AO1)   `4 marks`

....

....

....

....

c   Groundwater management (AO1)   `4 marks`

....

....

....

....

Energy security

Introductory ideas and concepts

Energy is available to us from many different sources including fossil fuels, nuclear power and various renewable energy forms.

⑱ What is the difference between primary and secondary energy? (AO1)   `4 marks`

....

....

....

....

....

We use energy in a variety of ways in our everyday lives, for heating, lighting and cooking in the home, for travelling, as well as for powering machinery and appliances used both domestically and in industry. These components of demand are usually classified into industrial, residential, commercial and transport uses.

⑲ What is meant by a country's 'energy mix'? (AO1)   `3 marks`

....

....

....

....

....

Relationship of supply to physical geography

20 Complete Table 5.2 to outline how the three different aspects of physical geography will influence the quantity and quality of energy supply. (AO1, AO2) `12 marks`

Table 5.2 Relationship between energy supply and physical geography

Aspect of physical geography	Influence on energy supply
Climate (4 marks)	
Geology (4 marks)	
Drainage (4 marks)	

Energy supply and globalisation

21 With reference to a named transnational corporation that you have studied, explain its role in the production, processing and distribution of energy. (AO1, AO2) `8 marks`

Sustainability issues and energy management

The future of the balance between population and energy resources depends very much on the potential to develop a sustainable energy supply and a sustainable level of consumption.

Whatever types of energy sources are used to supply energy needs, sustainability of energy can be increased by reducing the amount of energy consumed per person.

---

22 Assess the sustainability of strategies being used to increase the supply of energy in different parts of the world. (AO1, AO2)　　`10 marks`

23 With reference to examples, examine strategies for reducing energy consumption in ONE specific setting (*domestic* or *industrial and commercial* or in *transport*). (AO1, AO2)　　`10 marks`

Write your answers on a separate sheet of paper.

Mineral ore security

Sources, distribution and uses of specified ore

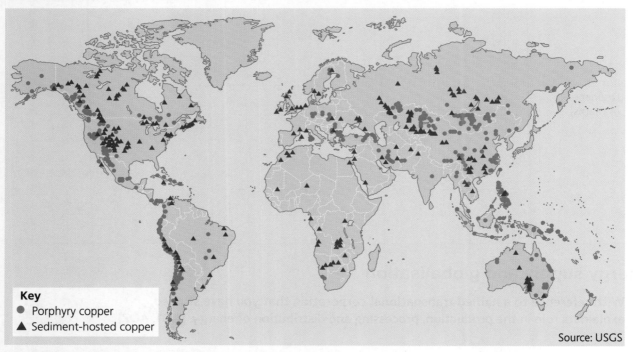

Key
- ● Porphyry copper
- ▲ Sediment-hosted copper

Source: USGS

Figure 5.2 Global distribution of copper ore deposits

---

24 Describe the distribution of copper ore deposits shown in Figure 5.2. (AO2, AO3)　　`4 marks`

....

....

....

....

25 For any specified mineral ore, identify its key qualities and outline its main uses in global commerce and industry. (AO1, AO2)　8 marks

Sustainability issues and environmental impacts

26 Compare the environmental impacts of traditional underground mining for ores with those of open-pit mining. (AO1, AO2)　6 marks

27 With reference to examples, discuss the sustainability issues associated with mineral ore extraction and processing. (AO1, AO2)　10 marks

Exam-style questions (A-level, Paper 2)

1 What is meant by the 'cut-off ore grade' in mineral ore extraction?
Circle the correct answer. (AO1)

A   This is the point at which all mining operations on a particular deposit are stopped because it is no longer economically viable to extract ore.

B   It is the lowest ore purity that can be exploited economically and it will vary depending on the mineral being extracted.

C   It is the amount of ore mined as a proportion of the amount of waste rock mined.

D   It is the measure of the purity of mineral content in a mineral ore reserve.

2 Explain how the environmental impacts of ore extraction might be minimised and made more sustainable. (AO1, AO2)

....

....

....

....

3 With reference to Figure 5.3 and your own knowledge, discuss the factors that influence energy mixes in contrasting settings. (AO1, AO2, AO3)

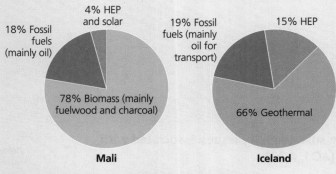

Figure 5.3 Energy mix contrasts in Mali and Iceland

....

....

....

....

....

....

....

....

4 'Fierce competition over water resources has prompted fears that water issues contain the seeds of violent conflict.' (Kofi Annan, former UN secretary general)

To what extent do you agree with this view? (AO1, AO2)

Write your answer on a separate sheet of paper.

Topic 6

Geography fieldwork investigation and geographical skills

This topic will be assessed at AS by written examination in AS Paper 2. Paper 2 will also assess your competence in a range of geographical skills, which should be developed as an integral part of your AS course when studying other topics. All students are required to undertake 2 days of fieldwork during their AS course.

At A-level, the fieldwork investigation is assessed by your submission of a written fieldwork report, which forms Component 3. All students are required to undertake fieldwork in relation to processes in both physical and human geography. Students must undertake 4 days of fieldwork during their A-level course.

At both AS and A-level, you need to be familiar with all stages of a fieldwork-based enquiry. Skills to be developed should include those involving qualitative data and quantitative data. This section outlines the stages of fieldwork investigation with a checklist of questions and will give some practice in samples from a range of geographical skills.

Geographical fieldwork investigation

1 Complete the blanks 1 to 7 below to give an appropriate title to each stage of the investigation process. (AO1)   `4 marks`

Any fieldwork investigation should be undertaken using scientific principles of investigation. There are a number of stages involved in carrying out such an investigation:

1 _____ setting out what you are trying to prove with your investigation

2 _____ deciding on an appropriate strategy for sampling:

- how you are going to collect your data (e.g. measure parameters)
- what, if any, secondary data may be needed to support your investigation

3 _____ calculating the risks to health and safety

4 _____ processing your results into a format that can be easily understood

5 _____ using statistical methods (usually) to analyse your results

6 _____ interpreting and drawing conclusions from your analysis

7 _____ understanding the strengths and weaknesses of your investigation

2 What is the aim of your fieldwork investigation? (AO2)   `2 marks`

_____

_____

_____

3 State both the hypothesis you set out to investigate and the null hypothesis. (AO2) 2 marks

....

....

4 Describe the location of your fieldwork and explain why the location is suitable to investigate your hypothesis. (AO2, AO3) 6 marks

....

....

....

....

....

....

....

....

....

....

Data collection methodology

The data collected for investigation will comprise both primary data and secondary data, some of each will be quantitative in nature and some qualitative.

5 In Table 6.1, distinguish between the primary and secondary data you are collecting and identify which data are quantitative in nature and which are qualitative. (AO1, AO2) 8 marks

Table 6.1 Types of data

	Quantitative	Qualitative
Primary data		
Secondary data		

6 Explain the meaning of sampling and why it is used to collect data. (AO1)   `3 marks`

....

....

....

There are three recognised types of sampling: random, systematic and structured.

7 In Table 6.2, outline the differences between random, systematic and stratified sampling, and compare the advantages and disadvantages of each type.
Make notes in the table below and then copy and complete the table on a separate sheet of paper. (AO1, AO2)   `18 marks`

Table 6.2 Sampling methods

Method	Outline of method	Advantages	Disadvantages
Random			
Systematic			
Stratified			

8 What other factors should be considered when collecting sample data? (AO3)   `4 marks`

....

....

....

....

9 Justify the relevance of the data you collected to proving your hypothesis. (AO2, AO3)   `4 marks`

....

....

....

....

10 Examine the health and safety risks associated with your investigation and suggest how you would reduce risks. (AO2, AO3) `6 marks`

....

....

....

....

....

....

Data analysis and presentation

The questions below continue with the theme of your fieldwork investigation.

11 Outline the secondary data that you used in your investigation and how they helped you to draw conclusions. (AO2, AO3) `4 marks`

....

....

....

12 Explain the advantages of a method that you used to analyse your data. (AO2, AO3) `5 marks`

....

....

....

....

13 With reference to one technique that you chose to present data in your investigation, justify the choice of this technique. (AO2, AO3) `6 marks`

....

....

....

....

....

14 To what extent did the findings of your investigation reflect your expectations at the start of the inquiry? (AO2, AO3) `5 marks`

....

....

....

....

Geographical skills

Core skills

Core geographical skills include the ability to explain geographical phenomena using annotated sketch maps, field sketches or photographs that record landscapes, landforms and associated geographical processes. In addition to demonstrating clear literacy and numeracy, an essential skill that geographers are expected to apply is the reading and interpretation of different types of maps, such as Ordnance Survey (OS) maps at different scales.

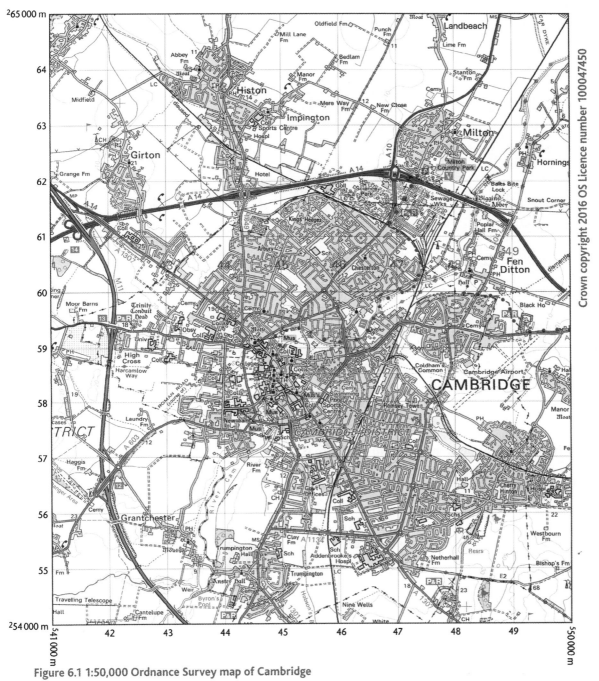

Crown copyright 2016 OS Licence number 100047450

Figure 6.1 1:50,000 Ordnance Survey map of Cambridge

15 On a separate sheet of paper draw a sketch of the map of Cambridge and its surroundings. Annotate the sketch to identify evidence of: (AO2, AO3)   `7 marks`

a   recent areas of growth areas on the rural urban fringe

b   the reasons why such locations are attractive as places to settle

c   older parts of the city

16 Annotate the photographs in Figure 2.3 on page 21 (in Topic 2 Changing places) to highlight contrasts is housing and residential areas.

6 marks

Cartographic skills

As well as being able to read and interpret OS maps, you are expected to interpret maps appearing in different forms such as weather maps, or those with proportional symbols or those showing movement such as flow lines or trip lines.

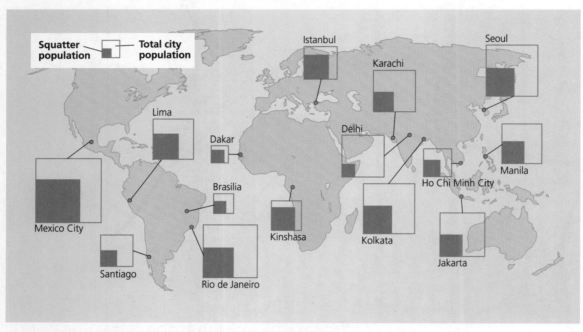

Figure 6.2 The size of the squatter population in selected world cities

17 Use the proportional symbol map shown in Figure 6.2.

a Which city has the largest proportion of squatters? (AO3)

1 mark

b Which city has the smallest proportion of squatters? (AO3)

1 mark

c Which city has the largest overall squatter population? (AO3)

1 mark

18 Describe the global pattern of squatter population in world cities. (AO3)

4 marks

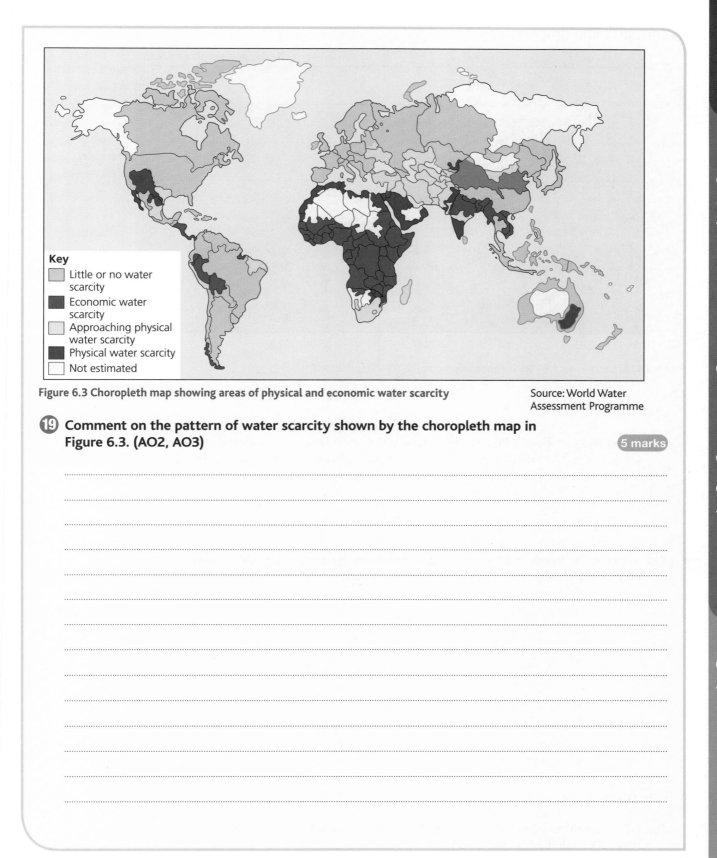

Figure 6.3 Choropleth map showing areas of physical and economic water scarcity

Source: World Water Assessment Programme

Key
- Little or no water scarcity
- Economic water scarcity
- Approaching physical water scarcity
- Physical water scarcity
- Not estimated

19 Comment on the pattern of water scarcity shown by the choropleth map in Figure 6.3. (AO2, AO3)

5 marks

....

....

....

....

....

....

....

....

....

....

....

....

....

Graphical skills

As with maps, graphs used to display geographic information and data take a variety of forms. These include line graphs, bar graphs, scattergraphs, pie charts and triangular graphs, as well as graphs with logarithmic scales and dispersion diagrams.

The questions and exercises in this section represent a sample of graphical skills you need to show and not the full range.

Compound line graphs

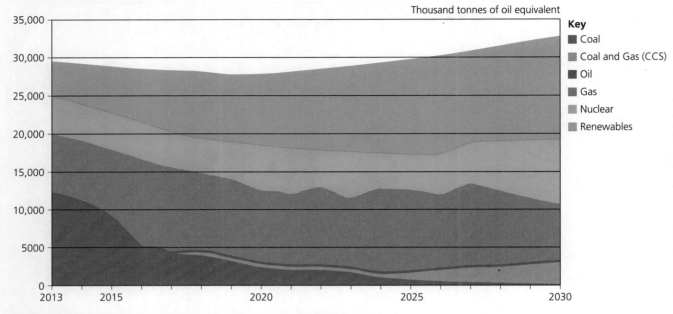

Figure 6.4 UK energy mix (electricity generation only), 2013–30 (predicted)

20 Using the compound line graph in Figure 6.4, estimate the predicted amount of (a) gas and (b) nuclear power that will be part of the UK's energy mix in 2025. (AO3) `2 marks`

....
....
....

21 Analyse the predicted trends in sources of energy used in the UK energy mix for electricity generation from 2013 to 2030 shown in Figure 6.4. (AO2, AO3) `5 marks`

....
....
....
....
....
....
....
....

Bar graphs

22 A histogram is a particular type of bar graph. In what ways does it differ from a simple bar graph? (AO1) `2 marks`

....
....
....

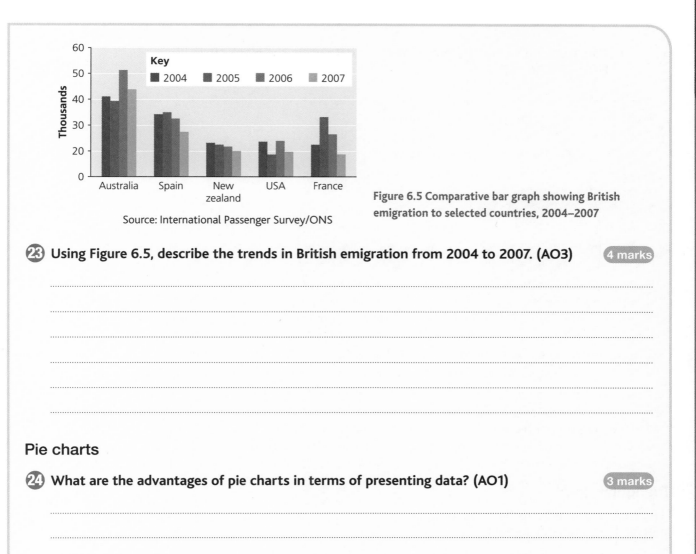

Figure 6.5 Comparative bar graph showing British emigration to selected countries, 2004–2007

Source: International Passenger Survey/ONS

23 Using Figure 6.5, describe the trends in British emigration from 2004 to 2007. (AO3)   4 marks

....

....

....

....

....

....

Pie charts

24 What are the advantages of pie charts in terms of presenting data? (AO1)   3 marks

....

....

....

....

Table 6.3 is fieldwork data recorded by students investigating channel characteristics. Channel bed pebbles were sampled at one site and categorised using Power's Scale of Roundness into the different classes shown in the table.

25 a Complete Table 6.3 by converting the data into percentages and then into degrees of a circle. (AO3)   6 marks

Table 6.3 Classes of roundness of channel bed pebbles from site 1 of stream investigation

	Category of roundness						
	Very angular	Angular	Sub-angular	Sub-rounded	Rounded	Well rounded	Total
Frequency	9	12	4	5	3	0	33
Percentage							
Degrees in pie chart							

b **Construct a pie chart to represent these data using the blank circle in Figure 6.6. (AO3)**

6 marks

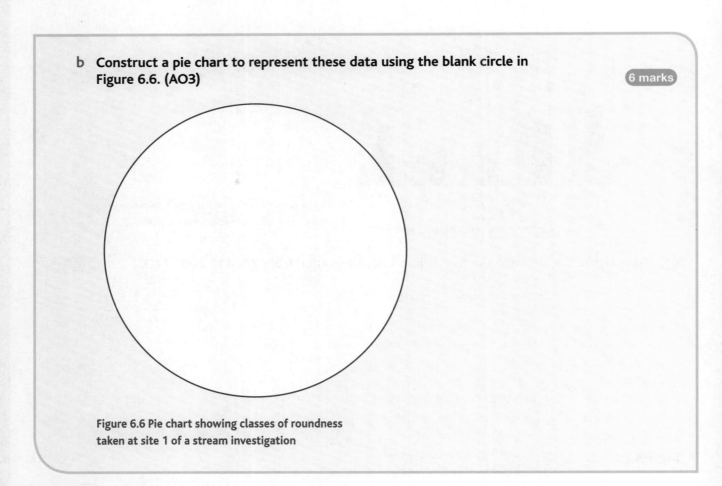

Figure 6.6 Pie chart showing classes of roundness taken at site 1 of a stream investigation

Triangular graphs

Figure 6.7 shows how to plot and interpret the data presented on a triangular graph.

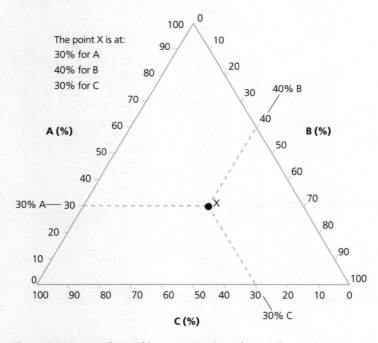

Figure 6.7 How to plot and interpret a triangular graph

Table 6.4 Percentage of electricity produced by three categories of generating source for five different countries

Country	% Thermal and others (including renewables)	% Nuclear	% Hydroelectric power
France	23	52	25
Norway	3	0	97
Sweden	22	30	48
UK	88	1	11
USA	74	14	12

26 Plot the data in Table 6.4 onto the blank triangular graph in Figure 6.8. (AO3) `5 marks`

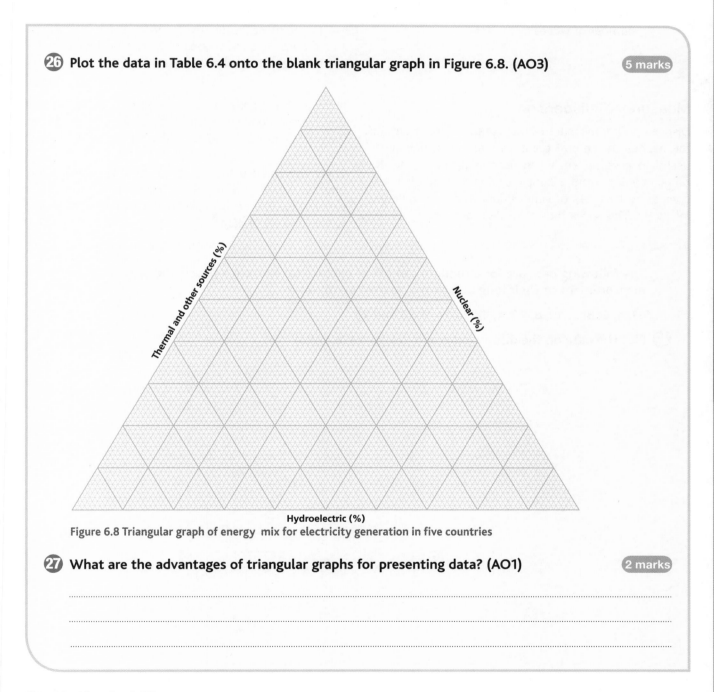

Figure 6.8 Triangular graph of energy mix for electricity generation in five countries

27 What are the advantages of triangular graphs for presenting data? (AO1) `2 marks`

....

....

....

Statistical skills

The most effective ways of analysing data from fieldwork investigations are by calculating measures of central tendency and measures of dispersion of the data or by applying statistical tests to measure the strength of correlation or distinct differences between sets of data.

28 Complete the three missing blank words to give names to the three measures of average. (AO1)

1 mark

Measures of central tendency

There are three measures in which an average value can be given to a set of measurements:

1 _____ = the average that is given when *all the values in a set of data are added together and then divided by the number of values in the set*

2 _____ = the average given to the middle value of a set of data when the data are 'ranked' in order of value from the highest to the lowest or from the lowest to the highest

3 _____ = the average assigned to the most frequently occurring value in a set of data — or, in classes of data, the class with the highest number of values in it

Measures of dispersion

Dispersion is a measure of the 'spread' of data around the average or central point. Measuring dispersion is useful to geographers when describing how wide the range of values from a sample is, and particularly when comparing two sets of similar data from two different locations. This gives the set of data an identity as the measurements collected can be very 'clustered' around the average showing all measurements are similar or they can be more spread out with a wide range of values.

There are three measures of dispersion: range, inter-quartile range and standard deviation. The range is simply the difference between the highest and lowest values in a set of data.

The following data are for a random sample of pebbles taken from a beach and are the measurement of their long axis to the nearest centimetre:

11, 4, 6, 8, 3, 10, 8, 10, 4, 12, 5, 14, 9, 13 and 22

29 Plot the data on the dispersion graph in Figure 6.9. (AO3)

3 marks

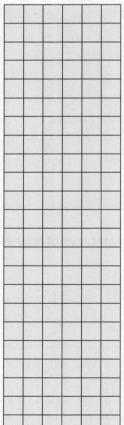

Figure 6.9 Dispersion graph of sample pebble sizes

30 Find the following values for this set of data. (AO3)   5 marks

a Range ....

b Median ....

c Upper quartile ....

d Lower quartile ....

e The inter-quartile range ....

31 Comment on the spread of pebble sizes in this sample. (AO3)   3 marks

....

....

....

....

The standard deviation is a statistically important measure of dispersion as it links the data set to the normal distribution. One standard deviation suggests that 68.2% of all values are within that value of the central measure (mean), so a small standard deviation value means that the data are clustered, whereas a higher standard deviation value indicates a wider dispersion of values.

A second set of sample pebbles were collected from another site on the same beach as shown in Table 6.5.

32 Using the data in Table 6.5, calculate the standard deviation for the long axis of the second set of pebbles collected. (AO3)   7 marks

Table 6.5 Sample of pebbles from second site and standard deviation table

Long axis of pebble collected in cm (x)	$x - \bar{x}$	$(x - \bar{x})^2$
1	−2.5	6.25
2	−1.5	2.25
2	−1.5	2.25
2	−1.5	2.25
2	−1.5	2.25
3		
4		
5	1.5	2.25
6	2.5	6.25
8		
$\sum x = 35$		$\sum(x - \bar{x})^2 =$
$\bar{x} = 3.5$		

Standard deviation formula = $SD = \sqrt{\dfrac{\sum(x - \bar{x})^2}{n}}$

So σ =

This means 1 standard deviation (68.2% if we assume there is a normal distribution) will be between _____ cm and _____ cm.

Inferential and relational statistics

Table 6.6 shows a list of ten countries with the infant mortality rate and the GDP per capita (US$) values for each country. The data suggest that there is an inverse relationship or negative correlation. Generally the higher the per capita income of the country, the lower the infant mortality and it seems feasible that richer countries can afford better healthcare systems so that more infants survive.

Table 6.6 Relationship between infant mortality rates and GDP per capita, 2015

Country	Infant mortality rate (per 1,000 live births per year)	GDP per capita (US$) PPP (= purchasing power parity)
Botswana	35	7,780
Brazil	15	8,668
China	9	8,055
India	38	1,580
Japan	2	32,594
Malaysia	6	9,768
Sudan	48	1,824
Thailand	11	6,015
UK	4	44,343
USA	6	55,850

Sources: World Bank and *The Economist*

One statistical method that can be used to measure the strength of this relationship is Spearman's rank correlation coefficient. This provides a numerical value (R_s) which summarises the degree of correlation and thus provides an objective indicator.

33 **Complete the Spearman's rank table (Table 6.7) by ranking each set of values from highest to lowest. Calculate the difference between each rank and then square the value for each. Sum all of the squared values. (AO3)** `5 marks`

Table 6.7

Country	IMR	Rank 1 (R1)	GDP/capita (US$)	Rank 2 (R2)	Difference R1 – R2	Difference squared (d^2)
Botswana	35		7,780			
Brazil	15		8,668			
China	9		8,055			
India	38		1,580			
Japan	2		32,594			
Malaysia	6		9,768			
Sudan	48		1,824			
Thailand	11		6,015			
UK	4		44,343			
USA	6		55,850			
					$\Sigma d^2 =$	

34 **Calculate R_s. (AO3)** `5 marks`

$$R_s = 1 - \left(\frac{6 \sum d^2}{n^3 - n} \right)$$

where n = number of paired values

Rs = _____

To find out whether this Spearman's rank value is statistically significant, you must compare it against the critical values at 0.05 level of significance (95% confidence) and at 0.01 level of significance (99% confidence).

35 Using the critical values provided in Table 6.8, assess the statistical significance of the calculated value of R_s. (AO3) `2 marks`

Table 6.8 Critical values for Spearman's rank coefficient with ten pairs of values

Number of paired data in sample	0.05 level of significance	0.01 level of significance
10	0.648	0.794

....

....

....

....

Exam-style questions (AS, Paper 2)

1 Explain the difference between primary and secondary data and why it is useful to use both sources when carrying out a fieldwork investigation. (AO2) `2` `2 marks`

....

....

....

....

2 You have experienced a fieldwork investigation as part of your course. Use your experience to answer the following questions. `6` `6 marks`

a   State the hypothesis on which your investigation was based.

....

....

b   Describe the methods used to collect primary data. (AO2, AO3)

....

....

....

....

....

....

....

....

....

3 Evaluate the success of your investigation and the extent to which it has improved your geographical understanding of the area you studied. (AO2, AO3)   10   9 marks

....
....
....
....
....
....
....
....
....
....

4 A group of students carried out an investigation to establish whether there is a relationship between distance from source (distance downstream) and discharge.

Their hypothesis was that discharge will increase with increasing distance downstream and their null hypothesis was that there would be no relationship.

The students tested for a correlation between the two sets of data shown in Table 6.9 using a Spearman's rank correlation coefficient calculation.

Table 6.9

Site	Distance from source	(a) Rank	Discharge (cumecs)	(b) Rank	Difference (d) = (a) − (b)	Difference² (d^2)
1	600	1	0.011	1	0	0
2	700	2	0.017	3	−1	1
3	1,300	3	0.014	2	1	1
4	1,400	4	0.023			
5	1,900	5	0.042	7	−2	4
6	2,000	6	0.019			
7	2,550	7	0.072	8	−1	1
8	2,650	8	0.041			
					$\sum d^2 =$	

Spearman's rank formula $= 1 - \left(\dfrac{6 \sum d^2}{n^3 - n} \right)$

a Complete Table 6.9 and the calculation of R_s (show your working). (AO1)   5   4 marks

$R_s =$

Table 6.10 shows an extract from the table of critical values for R_s.

Table 6.10

Number of paired data in sample	0.05 level of significance	0.01 level of significance
8	0.643	0.833

b   **How confident can you be that the students' hypothesis is supported by the data? (AO3)**

   2   2 marks

....

....

....

c   **Plot a scattergraph to show the relationship between distance from the source and discharge. (*This will be mostly completed in the exam.*) (AO3)**

   2   2 marks

   Draw your scattergraph on a separate piece of graph paper.

d   **To what extent does the evidence support the hypothesis that discharge will increase with increasing distance from the source? (AO2, AO3)**

   10   9 marks

....

....

....

....

....

....

....

....

....

....

....

....

....

....

....

....

....

....

....

Also available

...and many more

Go to **http://www.hoddereducation.co.uk/studentworkbooks** for details of all our student workbooks.

Hodder Education, an Hachette UK company, Blenheim Court, George Street, Banbury, Oxfordshire OX16 5BH

Orders

Bookpoint Ltd, 130 Park Drive, Milton Park, Abingdon, Oxfordshire OX14 4SB

tel: 01235 827827

fax: 01235 400401

e-mail: education@bookpoint.co.uk

Lines are open 9.00 a.m.–5.00 p.m., Monday to Saturday, with a 24-hour message answering service.

You can also order through the Hodder Education website: www.hoddereducation.co.uk

© Philip Banks and Paul Abbiss 2017

ISBN 978-1-4718-8369-9

First printed 2017

Impression number   8   7   6   5   4   3

Year   2022   2021   2020   2019   2018

This guide has been written specifically to support students preparing for the AQA A-level Geography examinations. The content has been neither approved nor endorsed by AQA and remains the sole responsibility of the authors.

Typeset by Aptara, India

Printed in Dubai

Hachette UK's policy is to use papers that are natural, renewable and recyclable products and made from wood grown in sustainable forests. The logging and manufacturing processes are expected to conform to the environmental regulations of the country of origin.

ISBN 978-1-4718-8369-9

9 781471 883699